This eBook covers the basics of EFT Tapping. For a more complete guide to EFT Tapping, please download "Healing, Transformation, and All Things EFT Tapping" on my website:

www.TessaCason.com

Tessa Cason
5694 Mission Ctr. Rd. #602-213
San Diego, CA. 92108
www.TessaCason.com
Tessa@TessaCason.com

LEGAL NOTICE AND DISCLAIMER:

From author and publisher: The information in this book is not intended to diagnose or treat any particular disease and/or condition. Nothing contained herein is meant to replace qualified medical or psychological advice and/or services. The author and publisher do not assume responsibility for how the reader chooses to apply the techniques herein. Use of the information is at the reader's discretion and discernment. The author and publisher specifically disclaim any and all liability arising directly or indirectly from the use or application contained in this book.

Nothing contained in this book is to be considered medical advice for any specific situation. This information is not intended as a substitute for the advice or medical care of a Physician prior to taking any personal action with respect to the information contained in this book. This book and all of its contents are intended for educational and informational purpose only. The information in this book is believed to be reliable, but is presented without guaranty or warranty.

By reading further, you agree to release the author and publisher from any damages or injury associated with your use of the material in this book.

400 EFT Tapping Statements™ for Being Empowered and Successful

Tessa Cason

Introduction

In 2000, as a Life Coach, I went searching for a tool or technique that could help my clients. Together, the clients and I would decide their homework and the tasks they would complete during the upcoming week. Even though the client knew what to do and wanted to do the tasks, somehow the tasks were not getting completed.

A book on EFT (Emotional Freedom Technique) Tapping was recommended as a potential tool to help my clients. How tapping your head would help my clients, I did not know.

I had some adventuresome clients (and forgiving if need be) that I taught how to tap. When **every single client** returned for their next appointment and shared how different their lives had been that week because of tapping, I took noticed!

I then put all my energy into understanding how tapping worked and how to work EFT.

Our lives don't change until we change the mis-beliefs, the dysfunctional beliefs on a subconscious level. EFT Tapping is one of the most powerful techniques I found that could do just that; change our beliefs on a subconscious level.

Now, EFT Tapping is my main go-to tool to assist my clients in changing the beliefs that prevent them from creating the reality they desire.

Tessa Cason

Table of Contents

Empowered, Personal Power

Being empowered is not about physical, brute strength. It is not about the number and height of our successes and accomplishments. It is not about fame, the house we live in, the car we drive, or the clothes we wear.

Being empowered is the strength,
substance, and character of our inner being.

It is knowing that whatever life throws at us, we will prevail.

All of us will have events that will challenge our ability to survive, physically, mentally, and emotionally. The manner in which we handle, survive, and grow from these challenges reveals how comfortable we are with being empowered. Below is one woman's story of discovering and learning how to be empowered.

As a working, single mom, Tiffany did the best she could raising her daughter Summer, who was now nearing the tween years. Six months previously, she had moved the two of them into the home of her boyfriend. Everything was going well...until the night she came home early to find her boyfriend molesting her daughter. At that instant, she grabbed her daughter, ran out the door, called the police, and took her daughter to the nearest hospital.

In an instant, Tiffany's and Summer's lives were changed forever. Working paycheck to paycheck, the financial resources were not immediately available to find a new home. She had to ask friends and family for assistance and support...a humbling experience for Tiffany. The situation stripped Tiffany of her self-confidence and her ability to trust others was shaken. Daily she suffered the shame of creating an unsafe environment for her daughter.

Yet, she realized she had a choice. She could be the victim, feel sorry for herself, or she could take responsibility. Tiffany took a deep breath and surrendered to what was and the current situation she found herself in.

Surrendering taught her about acceptance. Needing assistance from others taught her to be open to receive. She was grateful and surprised by the kindness of others and their willingness to help when she needed their help the most.

"This event shook me to my core," Tiffany said. "It was a huge wake-up call, a realization that I needed to live my life in Truth. I realized that the events themselves were neutral. What was important was my response to the events. I knew I didn't want more of what I had.

"My desire was for change so I could manifest a different life. It took mindful awareness, sometimes moment to moment, of how each choice felt to me. I had to weigh again the idea of 'If I put this out into the Universe, is this what I want back?' This daily, sometimes hourly, practice of constantly assessing and experimenting brought me great confidence and faith in my ability to handle anything. This gave me a tremendous amount of personal power."

After reflecting on her story, she added, "Knowing that I had the power of choice created a sense of peace for me. Though cash was in short supply, I felt blessed, thankful, and prosperous as a result of the generosity and graciousness of others."

Success

To each of us, success is different. Yet, there are common threads throughout all successes. Here are some of the common threads:

Successful people:

* Know what they want.

* Allow themselves to dream.

* Set goals and work toward their fulfillment.

* Have a detailed plan to accomplish their goals and dreams.

* Take action.

* Understand that setbacks and obstacles will teach them valuable lessons.

* Focus on solutions and are solution-oriented.

* Know everything they accomplish in life is up to them.

* Take complete responsibility for their lives.

* Don't quit or give up.

* Understand there is no guarantee they will succeed.

* Are flexible about the process of achieving their goals.

* Make decisions and continue to move forward.

* Continually reevaluate their plan.

* Accept change and adapt to difficulties.

* Are resilient and persistent.

* Believe in their success before success is visible.

* Are willing to accept feedback and self-correct.

* Are committed to the fulfillment of their dreams and goals.

* Live in the "now." They are present in their lives.

* Know that life is not a rehearsal for something else.

* Understand the seeds they plant today will be the rewards they will harvest tomorrow.

* Expect to meet many obstacles and difficulties along the way.

* Know that failure is only temporary, just part of the process.

* Pick themselves up after failure and press on.

Successful people are dreamers with their feet firmly planted in reality. The challenge of working toward their dreams and goals is just as exciting as the fulfillment of them. Overcoming each obstacle strengthens their resolve. Each lesson they learn from failure brings them closer to success. Their focus is on the goal. Successful people know they will succeed before there is evidence of their success.

Success is setting a goal, working their the fulfillment of their goals, and then feeling pride and satisfaction in their accomplishments.

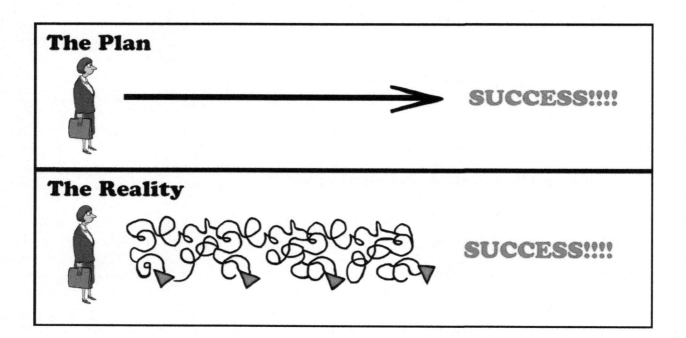

Being Empowered and Successful Qualities

Everyone's definition for success and power are unique to them. Here I offer qualities that might help you define success and power for yourself:

* Able to recognize, identify, and take ownership of the things about themselves they want to change
* Accepting
* Accepts compliments with grace
* Accountable
* Adaptable and flexible
* Allowing
* Appreciative
* Aware
* Be their own inspiration
* Being their authentic self
* Belief in self
* Capable
* Caring
* Charisma
* Charitable
* Clarity of values
* Clear vision of their life
* Clear, sharp mind
* Committed to themselves
* Commitment
* Communicates clearly and honestly
* Compassionate
* Competent
* Confident
* Congruent, walks their talk
* Completes tasks
* Conscious
* Considerate
* Consistent
* Constructive
* Content
* Courageous
* Creative
* Creative thinker
* Curious
* Determined
* Develop and practice new skill sets when needed
* Diplomacy
* Discerning

* Disciplined
* Drama-free
* Effective
* Embraces change
* Embraces possibilities
* Emotionally strong
* Emotionally mature
* Empathetic
* Empowers self and others
* Energetic
* Evaluates criticism
* Feels the fear and does it anyway
* Focused
* Follows their heart
* Follow-through
* Forgiving
* Giving
* Gracious
* Gratitude
* Grounded
* Happy
* Harmonious
* Has a plan to fulfill their vision and goals
* Honest
* Humorous
* Imaginative
* Inner core of strength
* Inner directed
* Inner motivated
* Insightful
* Inspiring
* Integrity
* Intelligent
* Joyful
* Kind
* Know one's value
* Knows their priorities
* Knows their strength and weaknesses
* Learns from their mistakes
* Listen to one's own wisdom

* Listens to others
* Lives their values
* Looks for solutions to problems
* Looks for the silver lining
* Loving
* Loyal
* Makes life an adventure
* Makes their own decisions
* Mature
* Motivated
* Nurturing
* Observant
* On purpose with life
* One with the Divine
* Open-mindedness
* Optimistic
* Organized
* Passionate
* Patient
* Peaceful
* Perceptive
* Perpetual student of knowledge
* Perseveres
* Persistent
* Physically fit
* Polite
* Positive
* Present time
* Problem-solver
* Principled

* Prioritizes health and well-being
* Purposeful
* Receptive
* Reflective
* Reliable
* Resilient
* Respectful of self and others
* Responsible
* Self-aware
* Self-assured
* Self-esteem
* Serene
* Sets goals
* Speaks truth
* Spiritual
* Successful
* Takes action
* Takes care of themselves, physically, mentally, and emotionally
* Takes responsibility for one's actions
* Teaches by Example
* Tenacity
* Thoughtful
* Trust their own intuition
* Truthful
* Visionary
* Warm
* Welcomes a challenge
* Willing to take calculated risks
* Wise

Ava's Story

After graduating from high school, Charlie's dad told Charlie he could continue to live at home, but he would be charged room and board. At 18 years old, Charlie was now financially responsible for himself.

After retrieving a bottle of water from the refrigerator and sitting down at the kitchen table next to Sophie, Ava asks, "Sophie, can we schedule a session for Saturday to continue?"

While spreading jam on her buttered toast, Sophie responds, "I do appreciate my roommate's willingness to help with my case study! Saturday works. This jam is scrumptious. Try some."

Ava pops an English muffin in the toaster, with a smile turns to Sophie and says, "I am so glad you decided to become an EFT Practitioner and for twisting my arm into being your volunteer."

In between bites, a laughing Sophie says, "Twisted your arm? Did I twist your arm? Guess I did."

"Yum. This jam is delicious." Ava asks, "Something new?"

"A friend of mine sells her jams at the farmer's market. Good, isn't it? She started her business about a year ago and sells out at every farmer's market. Speaking of businesses, how is the new business going with your sisters? Well, I hope. Or is that part of the reason to continue the sessions," asks Sophie.

"Well, you opened the floodgates when we worked on feeling emotions. I think maybe part of the reason I might have buried my feelings is because I didn't want to face how disempowered I have felt my whole life," says Ava.

"Wow. The whole 27 years of your existence?" Sophie teases.

"Well, it *was* a difficult childhood for me. Having an older sister that is beautiful, intelligent, talented, and an accomplished model that has been on countless number of magazine covers and a younger sister that is also very accomplished even though she is younger than I am. She's a tech whiz that sold her video game for millions," says Ava.

Standing up and carrying her dishes to the sink, Sophie teases Ava, "Most people would not call that a difficult childhood. You had loving parents, a beautiful home, and food on the table every night. So, the difficult part was being a middle daughter?"

Sitting back down at the table, Sophie waits for Ava to respond. Slowly Ava says, "I did have great parents. We did have a beautiful home. I could not compete with my sisters."

Sophie waits while Ava carries her dishes over to the sink. Turning around, leaning up against the sink, feeling very uncomfortable, Ava says, "Sophie, I could not compete with an older sister that was beautiful and a younger sister that was so smart. Then there was me, Average Ava." As tears fill Ava's eyes, she walks back to the table and sits down next to Sophie.

"Sophie," Ava says sadly, "I don't want to feel this way anymore."

"Oh, Ava, I get it. I do. We did work on feeling your emotions instead of ignoring and pretending they did not exist. There is a reason we bury our emotions. It's understandable what was buried is starting to surface. Plus, you are starting a new business with your sisters."

Heavy sigh from Ava. "That's the reason I want to continue the sessions." Sitting up straighter, making eye contact with Sophie, Ava says, "I want the business with my sisters to succeed. Yet, right now, I don't feel empowered. I don't feel powerful. Both my sisters are at a 10 with being empowered. I'm at a 1, maybe a 2."

"Ouch. Only a 1 or 2? We have some work to do."

With hopefulness in her voice, Ava says, "So you'll help me?"

Smiling, Sophie says, "Operation *Empowering Ava* starts now. Homework. For Saturday's session, think of three qualities of an empowered person that you think you lack."

Excitedly, Ava says, "Way cool! Operation *Empowering Ava* and three qualities. Got it."

Saturday morning, Ava starts off, "I did my homework. Three qualities I don't have: Confidence. With my sisters, they were always so confident. Number two. Belief in myself. Both of my sisters were determined to be a success in whatever they did. They knew they would succeed at whatever they set out to do. And thirdly, a sense of value. With my sisters, they each knew their value. I lack their confidence, belief in myself, and I'm not sure of my value."

As Ava spoke, Sophie writes down what Ava says:
* Lack of confidence.
* Lack of belief in self.
* Lack of value.

Ava waits for Sophie to finish writing and for her to comment. Thinking, Sophie asks, "Do you want to discuss any of these or do you just want to tap?"

"Just want to tap."

So together, Ava and Sophie tap:
* I lack the confidence to be empowered.
* I don't have unshakable confidence in my abilities.
* I lack the confidence to achieve my goals.
* I lack the confidence to be successful.
* I lack the confidence to be powerful.
* I don't believe I can be powerful.
* I don't believe in myself enough to be empowered.
* I lack the value being powerful requires.

After tapping, Ava takes a deep breath, exhales, and says, "I might have inched up to 3 on the empowered scale. It still seems so far from where my sisters are."

"Ava, we have only begun! I know it is difficult to be around other people that are powerful. It is the essence of who they are. But, with EFT Tapping, I think we can uncover the power you have buried within you."

Shifting in her chair, Ava asks, "You think I am powerful?"

"Ava, I believe we are all powerful, but for multiple reasons, our power gets buried deep within."

"What reasons do you think I buried my power?"

"As you said, you had two remarkable sisters you compare yourself to. With each session, we will explore a little deeper into you to find the reasons you buried your power. Think of each session as a power wash, removing the dirt that hides your power."

"I like that. EFT is like a power wash!" says Ava.

"Homework. Write a paragraph about power. Whatever comes to mind. Don't overthink it. Just write."

"Thanks, Sophie. I can do that. But, telling an editor not to edit, to write whatever comes to mind, might be a little difficult for me!"

Later in the week, Ava sits down at her computer and types:

Power. The thought of being powerful is overwhelming and scary. I'm not sure I'm willing to be powerful. Some powerful people are obnoxious and full of themselves. Some powerful people are bullies. I lack the drive that powerful people have. I lack the assertiveness that powerful people have. When I fail, I don't rebound. I guess I rationalize my failures and never seem to move past failure. I lack the drive and assertiveness that someone else that is powerful would have to be able to keep going when the going gets tough.

The following Saturday, at their session, Ava hands her typed paragraph to Sophie.

"This is great," says Sophie. "Not that it's typed, but what you have typed."

A little surprised, Ava says, "Really? I so wanted to edit it and make me sound more powerful. But, I tried to follow your instructions of writing what came to mind. Seems like I got stuck at failure. My sisters are soooooo successful and…"

Sophie finished Ava's sentence, "And by comparison, all you see are your failures and never your triumphs!"

"I'm a junior editor that works out of her home because the company doesn't have an office for me. Christine walks the runways for all the big name designers. Jenna sold the video game she designed for millions! I do feel like a failure," Ava says.

Sighing, Sophie says, "I know no matter what I say, you will argue with me. I could remind you of your successes but because they aren't grand enough, you see them as failures. So, instead, let's tap."

"I like tapping. I don't always feel good before tapping, but I do feel better the next day after the tapping has integrated," Ava says.

Looking at Ava's paragraph, Sophie says, "The paragraph you wrote can be made into tapping statements. So, we have our tapping statements."

* The thought of being powerful is overwhelming and scary.
* I'm not willing to be powerful.
* Some powerful people are obnoxious and full of themselves.
* Some powerful people are bullies.
* I lack the drive that powerful people have.
* I lack the assertiveness that powerful people have.
* I don't rebound from failure.
* I rationalize my failures.
* I never seem to be able to move past failure.
* I lack the drive and assertiveness of a powerful person.
* I'm not able to keep going when the going gets tough.

After tapping Sophie says, "On a scale of 1 – 10 with 10 high, where are you on the scale of feeling empowered?"

Sitting quietly, Ava checks in with herself. "Actually, I think I might be up to a five. I don't feel I am a failure any longer. But, I don't feel I can take on the world quite yet!"

"Cool. A five is good," says Sophie. "Homework. Another three qualities of a powerful person."

All week, Ava thinks about her homework. By Saturday, when Ava and Sophie start their next session, Ava says, "Did my homework. It's more difficult that I thought it would be. But, I did come up with three."

Sophie listens to Ava as she gets comfortable on their couch, putting a pillow on her lap and a tablet on top of the pillow. "And, those three qualities are? I'm ready to write."

"Well, thinking back to being a failure, if I change my perception and look for solutions instead of falling down and staying down."

"Humm," says Sophie. "Perception of what?"

"Okay. Good question. I guess, change my perception of myself for one. See myself as a problem solver instead of a victim and failure. Another would be to change my perception of the situation. Instead of seeing a situation as hopeless, switch to knowing there is a solution. And, thirdly, I guess, it's not a perception, but instead of staying down, stand up and keep moving."

A little surprised, Sophie says, "Wow. Okay, change perception of yourself and your perception of the situation. Cool. Number two quality would be?"

"In your office, you have a plaque that says, 'The best way to predict the future is to create it.' So, the second quality would be creativity. For me, I think that means not settling for the status quo and create a future that fulfills me."

After taking a sip of water, Sophie says, "Creativity. Creating a future that is fulfilling. I like this one. Okay. And, number three?"

Thinking, Ava says, "Well, look for solutions."

Confused, Sophie says, "Solutions? What do you mean exactly?"

"I have been known to kind of wallow and stay stuck, unable to move forward," says Ava.

Teasing Sophie says, "No? You wallow? Really?"

Laughing Ava says, "I know. I know. Me wallow? Okay. I'm taking ownership of my wallowing."

"Okay, Ms. Ava, instead of wallowing?"

"Yes, Ms. Sophie. Instead of wallowing, I need to change my mindset to one that looks for solutions. Become Sherlock. Search for solutions!"

"Sherlock, huh. Okay, Sherlock, let's do some tapping and handle the failure and wallowing."

* I set myself up to fail.
* I dwell on my defeats.
* I fall down and stay down.
* I am not a problem-solver.
* I panic in difficult situation.
* I don't shape my own destiny.
* My identity is of a failure and loser.
* I am powerless to create the life I want.
* I'm not able to creatively problem solve.
* I don't know how to find the solutions.

"Sophie? Tell me something," a puzzled Ava says.

"Sure, if I can."

Looking out the window, collecting her thoughts, Ava finally turns to Sophie and says, "Sophie, your degree in college was in Liberal Arts. You have been working with a nonprofit organization since college. And now, you are studying to be an EFT Practitioner. Do you think it will be worth all the effort you are putting into a possible career move without knowing if you will succeed?"

Taking a moment before she responds, Sophie finally answers, "I do think it will be worth it. Taking the courses, learning EFT, doing case studies, I've learned a lot. Whether I set up a practice and work full-time being a practitioner, I don't know yet. I love working at the non-profit," Sophie says.

Ava asks, "What will help you decide if you want to pursue being an EFT Practitioner?"

"Well," Sophie starts, "I'm not sure yet. I guess, I have to see what it feels like to be a practitioner."

"Sophie, you have been doing case studies. Isn't that somewhat the same as if you had a practice?"

"It is, somewhat," answers Sophie. "Do these questions have anything to do with you and your future with your sisters?"

Hesitating, Ava slowly says, "It does. I'm trying to decide how to move forward."

Surprised, Sophie says, "I thought it was a done deal. Are you having second thoughts? Is that part of the reason you wanted to work on being empowered and successful?"

Somewhat relieved, with a huge exhale Ava says, "Yes."

"Hummm, I see," Sophie says laughing.

"What's so funny?" an indignant Ava says.

"When you came home after the week with your parents and sisters, you were so excited. The three of you were going to build a business together. Christine wanted to design a website that allowed anyone to purchase clothes for their body type, taste, and occasion. Jenna was going to design a program that when someone came to the website, they could enter their specifics such as their height, measurements, skin tones, and a 3D avatar of them would materialize to try on the outfits. You were going to write the copy for the website and handle the day-to-day operations because your sisters didn't have the mentality for the day-in and day-out stuff."

Looking down at her hands, not wanting Sophie to see the tears escaping her eyes, she says, "Yup. That was the plan."

"Whoa. Wait. What? Was the plan? Did something happen that you haven't told me about?"

Still looking down, Ava whispers, "No. That's still the plan."

Gently Sophie says, "Ava, look at me."

Wiping the tears from her eyes, Ava lifts up her head and tries smiling.

Nearly whispering, Sophie says, "You want to explain?"

Sitting up straighter, getting a handle on her tears, Ava clears her throat and responds, "My sisters are so excited about the three of us doing the business. They're excited about the business and excited that we are doing it together."

Pondering, Sophie puts her hand under her chin, resting her elbow on her other arm. Then slowly, still thinking, she say, "Their excitement scares you because you think you will be the weakest member of the business and if the business fails, it will be your fault. Is that about it?"

"See. This is why you get the big bucks," answers Ava.

"Let me see if I have this right. The woman who graduated from college with honors and distinction, was snapped up by a publishing company the day she graduated from college, and has edited several books on the Best Selling Book List, is going to be the reason the business fails. Do I have that about right?" asks a stun Sophie.

A sad Ava says, "You forgot the Average Ava part and the woman who is only a junior editor."

"No, I didn't forget. Like your sisters, I don't see you as average. I see an exceptional woman that has accomplished a lot in her 27 years. Your family and I are all very proud of you. I guess you can't feel it because you don't see yourself like your family and I do. Ava, why do you think that is? And don't tell me because you had a beautiful sister that has graced the cover of numerous magazines or a clever sister that sold a video game for millions."

Ava starts to open her mouth, then realizes she can't answer because the answer had to do with Christine and Jenna.

Seeing Ava hesitate, Sophie says, "You were going to answer in relationship to your sisters! And, now that they can't be your excuse, you don't know the answer!"

Confused, Ava says, "Excuse? It is a legitimate answer!"

"Okay. Let's say it is. Let's move beyond that 'reason' and move on. Since I can see you don't have an answer, that's your homework. What's *another* reason you don't see yourself as your family and I do. Journal a least a paragraph or two. Same time next Saturday," says Sophie.

Ava had a difficult week, tossing and turning, thinking non-stop about her homework. *Why don't I see myself as a successful, powerful women that my family and my friends do?* When she sat down the following Saturday with Sophie, she still had no answer.

With her water bottle in hand, Sophie sits down on the couch, turns to Ava sitting across from her and says, "And?"

Laughing, Ava says, "That's the way you start off sessions?"

"For you, yes! And?"

Stalling for time, Ava takes a sip on water from her bottle. "And? Can I assume you are wanting the answer to my homework?"

"See, you are smart! Yes, I am wanting an answer to your homework."

"You know I tried Sophie. I really did."

Sophie stands up, walks over to Ava, and hands her a tablet and pen. "You have 15 minutes to write up an answer. I'm going to go wash our breakfast dishes. I expect a paragraph or two when I come back in this room in 15 minutes! And, not one word about one or both of your sisters!"

Watching Sophie march out of the room, Ava says rather loudly, "Really? Really?"

Looking down at the yellow paper, Ava gave herself permission to just write and not to edit.

I want a guarantee that if I try to be powerful, I will succeed. I think the reason I don't stand back up when I fail is because I will only fail again. Writing that I realize I am not committed to finding a way, committed to finding solutions. I think fear plays a role as well. I am afraid to be powerful. I think more will be expected of me if I was powerful. I would have to embrace opportunities. How can I embrace opportunities when I don't have a guarantee of success?

If I was powerful, I would have to be self-aware. I think I am too afraid to be self-aware. I think I am too frightened to identify my goals and vision. What if I am not smart enough, determined enough, tenacious enough to work toward my goals year after year after year? If I was powerful and self-aware, I might not fit in. Others might reject me because I no longer belong.

15 minutes later, Sophie walks into the room, takes the tablet from Ava, and sits back down on the couch across from her. The more she reads, the bigger her smile becomes. Then says, "This is excellent! If you will remember when we went over the pay-offs for not creating your reality, one of your top pay-off was 'guarantee.' And one of your top basic need is 'belonging.' Usually, wanting a guarantee is about a fear. For you, your fear is not belonging, a top basic need. So, you make yourself someone you think will be acceptable and not challenging for others so you can fit in and belong."

Ava listens to what Sophie is saying. After digesting what she said, she finally answers, "So, by not being successful and not being empowered, it doesn't challenge anyone. I'm just average and non-threatening."

With a huge smile on her face, Sophie says, "Exactly! You refer to yourself as Average Ava."

"So, when I fail down and stay down, I am less threatening and because everyone fails, it is easier to relate to me. Right?

"Exactly!"

Ava sits still for a while thinking of this ah-ha. When Sophie sees that Ava has a grasp of this concept, she asks, "Ava, what is your second pay-off? Do you remember?"

"I think I do. It was avoidance, right?"

"Correct," says Sophie. "Avoidance."

As if a light bulb went off in Ava's head, her face lights up and she says, "So, when I fail and stay down, I am avoiding being successful and powerful."

Triumphantly Sophie says, "Exactly."

"Huh," says Ava.

"Ava, what is your second top basic need? Do you remember?"

Thinking hard, Ava finally says, "No. I don't."

"Being unique and accomplishments," answers Sophie.

Letting the answer sink in, Ava finally says, "My two top needs are somewhat in conflict with each other, aren't they?"

"Yup. And, that's why you wanted to work on this issue of being empowered and being powerful. It wasn't about your sisters. It is about your need of being unique and achieving. These qualities are required of you at this time with the new business venture with your sisters."

Sitting quietly, Ava thinks. She takes a sip of her water while her brain tries to process all the new information. Sophie sits quietly as well, not wanting to interrupt Ava's thought process.

Finally, Ava says, "I think I get it. Having a need for belonging, I have allowed my pay-offs of guarantee and avoidance to dominate my need for accomplishment. My motivation has changed now that my sisters and I are starting a new business venture. Now, I want to accomplish and be unique. I have never allowed this need to be fulfilled because the belonging overpowered the accomplishment need. But, now that need is taking a back seat to wanting to succeed with my sisters."

Nodding her head in agreement, Sophie then says, "Yes and no."

"Yes and no?" asks Ava. "Huh?"

"Ava, you do have accomplishments. You graduated from college with honors, top of your class. You have edited books that have been on the best seller's list. You do have accomplishments."

"So, now I am confused," Ava says puzzled.

"I know. It seems confusing. You have accomplished a great deal but yet, you never *allowed* yourself to *acknowledge* those accomplishments because you wanted to fit in," comments Sophie. "Your family and I know of your accomplishments and thus, we see you differently than you have see yourself."

"Wow. Mind blowing. You're right. I have not wanted to acknowledge my accomplishments. I wanted to belong and not wanted anyone to feel less than me."

After taking another sip of water, Sophie says, "Ready to do some tapping? The two paragraphs

you wrote can be made into tapping statements."
"Oh, so ready!" Taking a sip of water, she then says to Sophie, "Let's begin!"

And so they tapped:

* I want a guarantee that if I try to be powerful, I will succeed.
* I am afraid to be powerful.
* More will be expected of me if I was powerful.
* I want a guarantee that I will succeed if I try.
* I am too afraid to be self-aware.
* I am too frightened to identify my goals and vision.
* I might not fit in if I was powerful.

For the next month, Sophie and Ava meet every Saturday to work through Ava's issues of being powerful and successful. Each week Ava stepped more into her power and was thankful for EFT Tapping.

One Saturday, about three months after Ava and Sophie began *Empowering Ava*, Sophie sits down on the couch. Entering the room, Ava says, "New plan for today."

Confused, Sophie says, "Oh?"

"Yup. Today, we are celebrating." Excitedly Ava says, "The website is completed. I feel better than I have ever felt. You, Sophie, are amazing, and I want to thank you for so many things. My sisters will be here in about an hour and the food is being delivered not long afterwards."

On the way out of the room Sophie says, "Cool! I am up for a celebration *after* I change clothes and put on some makeup!"

Beliefs and the Subconscious Mind

Everything in our life is a direct result of our beliefs.

A belief is a mental acceptance of and conviction in the truth, actuality, or validity of something. It is what we believe to be true, whether it is Truth or not. A belief is a thought that influences energy all the time.

A mis-belief, a dysfunctional belief is a belief that takes us away from peace, love, joy, stability, acceptance, and harmony. It causes us to feel stressed, fearful, anxious, and/or insecure.

The reason we aren't successful, happy, or prosperous has to do with our beliefs. Our beliefs determine our thoughts and feelings. Our thoughts and feelings determine our choices and decisions as well as our actions and reactions. Beliefs, then, precede all of our thoughts, feelings, choices, decisions, actions, reactions, and experiences.

Beliefs **precede** all of our thoughts, feelings, decisions, choices, actions, reactions, and experiences...

Our beliefs **determine** our thoughts.
Our thoughts **determine** our feelings.
Our thoughts and feelings **determine** our choices and decisions.
Our thoughts and feelings **determine** our actions and reactions.

Can you determine someone's beliefs from their actions and reactions? Persons A, B, C, and D just received a compliment that they looked nice today.

Person A responds:

Person B responds:

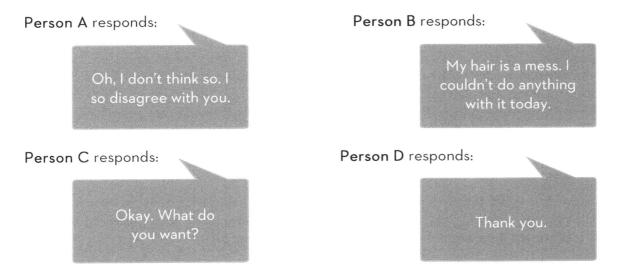

Oh, I don't think so. I so disagree with you.

My hair is a mess. I couldn't do anything with it today.

Person C responds:

Person D responds:

Okay. What do you want?

Thank you.

Person A: Totally disagrees. They don't think they look nice today. Person A definitely has self-esteem and self-worth issues. When we are not able to accept a compliment, it's a slap in the face for the person giving the compliment. It's as if Person A is saying, "If you think I look nice, your opinion sucks."

Person B: Cannot nor will not accept the compliment. They defect the compliment with a reason why they couldn't look nice. They justify their reason for not accepting the compliment. Think there might be a little bit of anger and/or shame in this type of response?

Person C: They think there are strings attached to the compliment. Anyone that would compliment them must want something. Might trust and discernment be an issue for them?

Person D: Well, if the response is genuine, then we know they have a healthy self-esteem and self-worth. If the response was said with arrogance, like "Naturally I look nice today" then we could either have someone who really is arrogant or someone who is insecure and using arrogance to hide the insecurity.

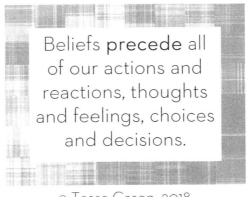

Beliefs **precede** all of our actions and reactions, thoughts and feelings, choices and decisions.

Subconscious Mind

The Conscious Mind

The conscious mind is that part of us that thinks, passes judgements, makes decisions, remembers, analyzes, has desires, and communicates with others. It is responsible for logic and reasoning, understanding and comprehension. The mind determines our actions, feelings, thoughts, judgements, and decisions **based on the beliefs.**

The Subconscious Mind

The subconscious is the part of the mind that is responsible for all of our involuntary actions like heart beat and breathing rate. It does not evaluate, make decisions, or pass judgment. It just is. It does not determine if something is "right" or "wrong."

The subconscious is much like the software of a computer. On the computer keyboard, if we press the key for the letter "a," we will see the letter "a" on the screen, even though we may have wanted to see "t."

Just as a computer can only do what it has been programmed to do, we can only do as we are programmed to do. Our programming is determined by our beliefs.

Our beliefs and memories are stored in the subconscious.

If we want to make changes in our lives, we have to change the programming, the mis-beliefs in the subconscious.

3 Rules of the Subconscious Mind

Three rules of the subconscious mind include:

1. Personal. It only understands "I," "me," "myself." First person.

2. Positive. The subconscious does not hear the word "no." When you say, "I am not going to eat that piece of cake," the subconscious mind hears "Yummm! Cake! I am going to eat a piece of that cake!"

3. Present time. Time does not exist for the subconscious. The only time it knows is "now," present time. "I'm going to start my diet tomorrow." "Tomorrow" never comes thus the diet is never started.

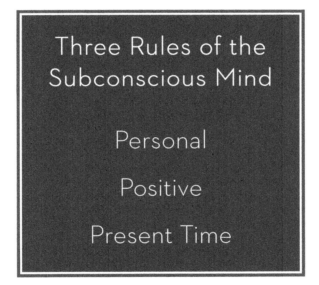

Three Rules of the Subconscious Mind

Personal

Positive

Present Time

EFT Tapping – Emotional Freedom Technique

If we want to make changes in our lives, long-lasting, permanent, constructive changes, we have to change the destructive, dysfunctional, mis-beliefs in the subconscious. We have to change the programming in the subconscious.

EFT Tapping changes dysfunctional, mis-beliefs on a subconscious level.

What is EFT – Emotional Freedom Technique:

EFT is a technique that allows us to change dysfunctional beliefs and emotions on a subconscious level. It involves making a statement while tapping different points along meridian paths.

The general principle behind EFT is that the cause of all negative emotions is a disruption in the body's energy system. By tapping on locations where a number of the different meridians flow, we are able to release unproductive memories, emotions, and beliefs which cause the blockages.

EFT Tapping Statements:

An EFT statement has three parts to it:

Part 1: Starts with "**Even though,**" followed by

Part 2: A statement which could be the **dysfunctional emotion or belief,** and

Part 3: Ends with "**I totally and completely accept myself.**"

A total statement would be "**Even though, I crave sweets, I totally and completely accept myself.**"

The instructions below are described if you were using your right hand. Reverse directions to tap using the left hand. It is only necessary to tap one side. Tapping both sides does not add any additional benefit.

I. Begin with circling or the Karate Chop Point (See next page):

A. With the fingertips of your right hand, find a tender spot below your left collar bone. Once you have found the tender spot, with your right fingertips, press firmly on the spot, make a circular motion toward the left shoulder, toward the outside, clockwise.

B. As your fingers are circling and pressing against the tender spot, make the following statement 3 times: "Even though,___[mis-belief statement]___, I totally and completely accept myself." An example would be: "Even though, I fear change, I totally and completely accept myself."

II. Tapping:

A. After the third time, tap the following 8 points repeating the [mis-belief statement] each time with each point. Tap each point 7 – 10 times:

1. The inner edge of the eyebrow just above the eye. [I fear change.]

2. Temple, just to the side of the eye. [I fear change.]

3. Just below the eye (on the cheekbone). [I fear change.]

4. Under the nose. [I fear change.]

5. Under the lips. [I fear change.]

6. Under the knob of the inside edge of the collar bone. [I fear change.]

7. 3" under the arm pit. [I fear change.]

8. Top back of the head. [I fear change.]

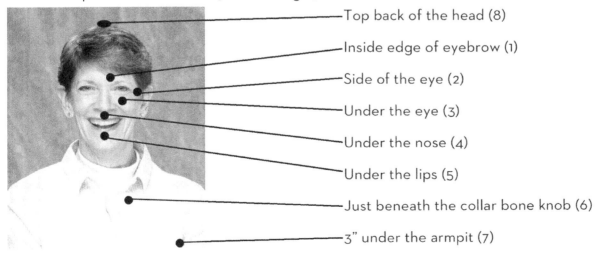

Top back of the head (8)

Inside edge of eyebrow (1)

Side of the eye (2)

Under the eye (3)

Under the nose (4)

Under the lips (5)

Just beneath the collar bone knob (6)

3" under the armpit (7)

B. After tapping, take a deep breath. If you are not able to take a deep, full, satisfying breath, do eye rolls.

III. Eye rolls

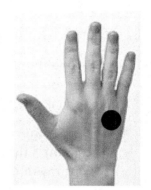

A. With one hand, tap continuously on the **back** of the other hand between the 4th and 5th fingers.
B. Head is held straight forward, eyes looking straight down.
C. For 6 seconds, roll your eyes from the floor straight up toward the ceiling while repeating the statement. Keep the head straight forward, only moving the eyes.

IV. Take another deep breath.

Karate Chop Point (KCP):

For the set up in EFT Tapping, use either the circling or the KCP. It is a matter of preference. One is not more effective than the other.

To tap the KCP, use the fingertips of the opposite hand or the KCP of both palms can be tapped together.

Tapping Points for the Short Form of EFT Emotional Freedom Technique

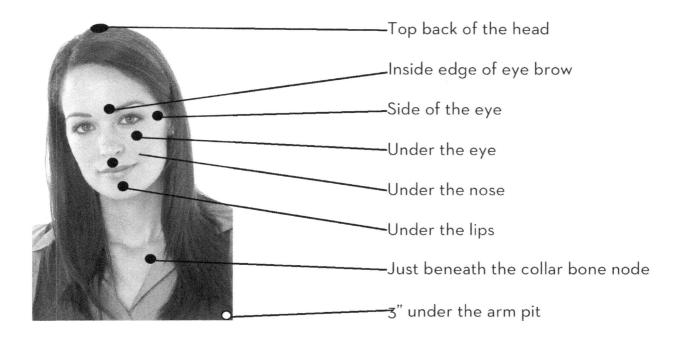

Top back of the head

Inside edge of eye brow

Side of the eye

Under the eye

Under the nose

Under the lips

Just beneath the collar bone node

3" under the arm pit

Yawning and Taking a Deep Breath

From Oriental medicine, we know that when Chi (energy) flows freely through the meridians, the body is healthy and balanced. Physical, mental, and/or emotional illness can result when the energy is blocked.

Dysfunctional beliefs and emotions produce blocks along the meridians, blocking energy from flowing freely in the body.

With EFT tapping, as we tap, we are releasing the blocks. As blocked energy is able to flow more freely, the body is now able to "breathe a sigh of relief." Yawning is that sigh of relief.

If, after tapping, we are able to take a complete, deep, full, and satisfying breath, we know that an EFT tapping statement has cleared. This yawn is an indication that an EFT tapping statement has cleared.

If the yawn or breath is not a full, deep breath then the statement didn't clear completely.

Integration...What Happens After Tapping

After tapping, our system needs some downtime for integration to take place. When the physical body and the mind are "idle," integration can then take place.

Sometimes, in the first 24 hours after tapping, we might find ourselves vegging more than normal, sleeping more than normal, or more tired than normal. This downtime is needed to integrate the new changes.

After installing a new program into our computer, sometimes we have to reboot the computer (shut down and restart) for the new program to be integrated into the system.

After tapping, our bodies need to reboot. We need some downtime. When we sleep, the new changes are integrated.

Healing begins naturally after the body has had a chance to integrate.

Sometimes after tapping, we forget the intensity of our pain and think that our feeling better had nothing to do with the tapping. Something so simple could not possibly create the improvement in our state of mind!

When we cut our finger, once it is healed, we don't even remember cutting our finger. As we move toward health, wealth, and well-being, sometimes we don't remember how unhappy, restless, or isolated we once felt.

How Does EFT Tapping Work?

1. Acceptance: The last part of the tapping statement we say, "I totally and completely accept myself." **Acceptance brings us into present time.** We can only heal if we are in present time. Laughter brings us into present time. "Laughter is the best medicine."

2. Addresses the current mis-belief on a subconscious level: In order to make changes in our lives, we have to change the dysfunctional beliefs, the mis-belief on a subconscious level. The middle part of the tapping statements are the "instructions" for the subconscious. **In order to make changes in our lives, we only care what the subconscious hears.**

3. Pattern interrupt: Dysfunctional memories and/or mis-beliefs disrupt or block the flow of energy from flowing freely along the meridians. Tapping is a pattern interrupt that disrupts the flow of energy to allow our **body's own Infinite Wisdom to come forth for healing.**

4. Mis-direct: One role of the physical body is to protect us. When our hand is too close to a flame, the body automatically pulls the hand back to safety. An EFT Tapping statement that agrees with the current belief is more effective. The physical body is less likely to "sabotage" the tapping if it agrees with the current belief.

An Example: The very first tapping statement we need to tap is: "It is not okay or safe for my life to change." Even though our lives are constantly changing does not mean we are comfortable or okay with change. When we are not comfortable with change, it creates stress for the body.

EFT Tapping Statement: "It is not okay or safe for my life to change."

* This statement appeases the physical body since it agrees with the current belief.
* The subconscious hears, "It is okay and safe for my life to change."
* The tapping disrupts the energy flow so our Truth can come forth.

The body will always gravitate to health, wealth, and well-being when the conditions allow it. EFT Tapping weeds the garden so that the blossoms can bloom more easily and effortlessly.

Science and EFT Tapping Research

EFT has been researched in more than 10 countries by more than 60 investigators whose results have been published in more than 20 different peer-reviewed journals. Two of the leading researchers are Dawson Church, Ph.D. and David Feinstein, Ph.D.

Dr. Dawson Church, a leading expert on energy psychology and an EFT master, has gathered all the research information and can be found on this website: www.EFTUniverse.com.

Two Research Studies Discussed Below

Harvard Medical Schools Studies and the Brain's Stress Response

Studies at the Harvard Medical School revealed that stimulating the body's meridian points significantly reduced activity in a part of the brain called the amygdala.

The amygdala can be thought of as the body's alarm system. When the body is experiencing trauma or fear, the amygdala is triggered and the body is flooded with cortisol also know as the "stress hormone." The stress response sets up an intricate chain reactions.

The studies showed that stimulating or tapping points along the meridians such as EFT tapping, drastically reduced and/or eliminated the stress response and the resulting chain reaction.

Dr. Dawson Church and Cortisol Reduction

Another significant study was conducted by Dr. Dawson Church. He studied the impact an hour tapping session would have on the cortisol levels of 83 subjects. He also measured the cortisol levels of people who received traditional talk therapy and the cortisol levels of a third group who received no treatment at all.

On an average, for the 83 subjects that completed an hour tapping session, cortisol levels were reduced by 24% reduction. Some subjects experienced a 50% reduction in cortisol levels.

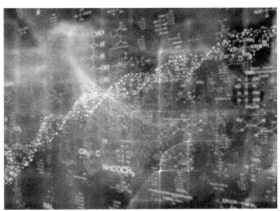

Subjects that completed an hour long traditional talk therapy and the subjects that had completed neither sessions did not experience any significant cortisol reduction.

Benefits of Using EFT Tapping

* The last part of the statement is "I totally and completely **accept** myself." **Acceptance** brings us into present time. Healing can only take place when we are in present time.

* By tapping, we are **calling forth our truths**. The key word here is "**our**." Not anyone else's. If my name is "Lucas," tapping the statement "Even though my name is Troy," my name will not be changed to Troy.

* Tapping **calls forth our own body's Infinite Wisdom**. When we cut our finger, our body knows how to heal the cut itself. Once the dysfunctional emotions, experiences, and beliefs have been "deleted," our body **automatically** gravitates to health, wealth, wisdom, peace, love, joy...

* By changing the mis-beliefs and dysfunctional emotions on a subconscious level, the changes we make with EFT are **permanent.**

* By tapping, we are "**neutralizing**" the stored memories that have been blocking energy from flowing freely along the meridians.

* Another benefit of tapping and EFT is desensitization. Let's say, we have a difficult person in our life that ignores us and/or criticizes us and we tap the statement: "This difficult person [or their name] ignores and criticizes me."

Tapping doesn't mean they will no longer ignore and/or criticize us.

It can, though, **desensitize us** so we no longer are affected by their behavior. Once we are desensitized, our perception and mental thinking improves. We are better able to make informed decisions. We don't take and make everything personally. Our health is not negatively impacted. Our heart doesn't beat 100 beats/minute. Smoke stops coming out of our ears. And our faces don't turn red with anger and frustration.

The Very First EFT Tapping Statement to Tap

The very first EFT tapping statement I have clients and students tap is "It is not okay or safe for my life to change." I have muscle tested this statement with more than a thousand people. Not one person tested strong that is was okay or safe for their life to change.

How effective can EFT or any therapy be if
it isn't okay or safe for our lives to change?

Since our lives are constantly changing, if it is not okay or safe for our lives to change, every time our lives change, it creates stress for the body. Stress creates another whole set of issues for ourselves, our lives, and our bodies.

Intensity Level

One measure of knowing how much an "issue" has been "resolved" is to begin, before tapping, by giving the issue an intensity number between 1 – 10, with 10 being high.

For example, you want a romantic partnership yet, you haven't met "the one." Thinking about the likelihood of a romantic relationship happening for you, how likely, on a scale of 1 – 10, with 10 being very likely and 1, not likely at all, would a romantic relationship happen for you?

Okay. You gave yourself a 2. Now let's start tapping!

When asked what the "issues" might be, "Well," you say. "It doesn't seem as if the people I want, want me."

Great tapping statement. So, you tap out, "Even though, the people I want don't want me, I totally and completely accept myself." After tapping you check in with yourself, the Intensity Level (IL) has gone up to a 4, a little bit more likely.

What comes to mind now? You say, "No one will find me desirable." Great tapping statement. You tap out, "Even though, no one will find me desirable, I totally and completely accept myself." Check the IL. How likely? Now you are at a 5. Cool! Progress.

What comes to mind now? You say, "I'm not comfortable being vulnerable in romantic relationships." Great tapping statement. You tap out, "Even though, I'm not comfortable being vulnerable in a romantic relationship, I totally and completely accept myself." Check the IL. Now it is a 6. Still progress.

What comes to mind now? "Well, it feels like if I am in a relationship, I will lose a lot of my freedom." Make this into a tapping statements. "Even though, I will lose my freedom when I am in a relationship, I totally and completely accept myself." The IL has gone up to a 7.

What comes to mind now? "Oh, if I was in a relationship, I would have to be accountable to someone!" Make this into a tapping statement: "Even though, I would have to be accountable to someone if I was in a relationship, I totally and completely accept myself." Wow...the IL is 9, very likely!

GIVING AN ISSUE AN INTENSITY LEVEL GIVES US AN INDICATION OF THE PROGRESS WE ARE MAKING WITH RESOLVING AND/OR HEALING THAT ISSUE IN OUR LIVES.

Using a Negative EFT Tapping Statement

Our beliefs **precede** all of our thoughts, feelings, decisions, choices, actions, reactions, and experiences...

If we want to make changes in our lives, we have to change the mis-beliefs, the dysfunctional beliefs. Our beliefs are stored in the subconscious.

To change our lives, to change a belief, we only care what the subconscious hears when we tap. The subconscious does not hear the word "no." When we say, "I am not going to eat that piece of cake," the subconscious hears, "Yummm, cake!"

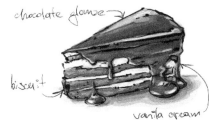

Example, if we don't believe we had what it takes to be successful and we tap the statement, "I have what it takes to be successful," the body could sabotage the tapping. We could tap and it won't clear.

If instead the statement we make is "I don't have what it takes to be successful," the "**not**" appeases the physical body and the subconscious hears, "I have what it takes to be successful!"

A statement with the word
"no" or "not,"
although may seem to
be contradictory, works best!

Finishing Touches (Optional)

If we tap a statement that the body knows not to be true, the tapping statement may not clear. As discussed with the Affirmation section on page 27, first we need to tap the affirmation with the "no" inserted in the tapping statement.

Part 1 of Finishing Touches – Read the statements on the following page. If one or more of the statements doesn't feel true yet, then you might want to do one round of the statements by inserting a "no" into the statement.

Part 2 – Some like to finish their tapping with statements that are centering and calming. If this is you, then you might want to try the 16 statements below and/or make up those that you like. The statements below can be said in any order that works for you.

Tapping Location	Statement
Eyebrow	All is well in my life.
Temple	Every day in every way I am getting better and better.
Under the Eye	I am fulfilled in every way, every day.
Under the Nose	My blessings appears in rich appropriate form with divine timing.
Under the Lips	I am an excellent steward of wealth and am blessed with great abundance.
Under the Collarbone Knob	I take complete responsibility for everything in my life.
Under the Arm	I have all the tools, skills, and abilities to excel in my life.
Top back part of the Head	I know I will be able to handle anything that arises in my life.
Eyebrow	All my dreams, hopes, wishes, and goals are being fulfilled each and every day.
Temple	Divine love expressing through me, now draws to me new ideas.
Under the Eye	I am comfortable with my life changing.
Under the Nose	I am able to create all that I desire.
Under the Lips	I know what needs to be done and follow through to completion.
Under the Collarbone Knob	My health is perfect in every way, physically, mentally, emotionally, and spiritually.
Under the Arm	I invite into my subconscious Archangel Raphael to heal all that needs to be forgiven, released, and redeemed. Cleanse me and free me from it now.
Top back part of the Head	The light of God surrounds me. The love of God enfolds me. The power of God protects me. The presence of God watches over and flows through me.

How to Use This Book

1. The statements are divided into sections. Read through the statements in one section. As you read a statement, notice if you have any reaction to the statement or feel the statement might be true for you. If so, note the number for that statement.

2. Once you have completed reading all the statements in one section, go back and reread the statements you noted and rate them on a scale of 1 – 10, with 10 being a biggie."

3. List the top statements.

4. From this list, select one and describe how it plays out in your life. It is important to recognize and identify the pattern. What are the consequences of having this mis-belief? Is there a trigger? How does it begin? How does it benefit you? How has it harmed you? There will be a different example listed in each section.

5. Tap out the statements. Statements can be combined for scripts...a different statement on each of the different tapping points in one round of tapping.

6. Describe any flashbacks or memories that you might have had as you were tapping out the statements. Describe any ah-has, insights, and/or thoughts you might have had as a result of tapping the statements.

7. After tapping all the statements, review them to determine if you still have a reaction to any of the statements. If you do, you have several options. One, put a "Why" before the statement. Tap out the answer. Secondly, note that this statement may not have cleared and continue on to the next section. Most likely, after additional statements are tapped, statements that may not have cleared, will clear without having to tap the statement again.

8. Allow some downtime for integration and for the body to heal.

9. The number of sections you do at a time will be up to you. Initially, you might want to do one section to determine if you get tired and need to have some downtime after tapping.

10. The day after tapping, again review the statements you tapped to determine if you still have a reaction. If you do, follow the instructions in #7.

1 – 20 EFT Tapping Statements

Those on top of the mountain did not fall there.
Marcus Washling

1. Power is destructive.

2. It is lonely at the top.

3. I dwell on my defeats.

4. I choke under pressure.

5. I rationalize my failures.

6. I don't expect to succeed.

7. Success is not sustainable.

8. I am not a problem-solver.

9. I lack the drive to succeed.

10. I don't focus on the results.

11. Power is the root of all evil.

12. I allow myself to be bullied.

13. Loss is the signal to give up.

14. I am paralyzed by my losses.

15. Setbacks mean I have failed.

16. It's too scary to be powerful.

17. I panic in difficult situations.

18. I don't love what I am doing.

19. I need others to motivate me.

20. I run as soon as I see trouble.

Journaling Pages for Statements 1 – 20

Ships are safe in the harbor, but that's not what ships are for.

William Shedd

1. From the tapping statements between 1 – 20, list the top seven statements that you thought or felt applied to you:

1.

2.

3.

4.

5.

6.

7.

2. From this list of seven statements, select one and describe how it plays out in your life. Give an example or two. It is important to recognize and identify the pattern. Is there a trigger? How does it begin? How has it benefited you? How has it harmed you? For instance, do setback mean you have failed? Thomas Edison said this about inventing electricity: I have not failed. I've just found 10,000 ways that won't work.

3. Tap out the top 7 statements.

4. As you were tapping out the statements, did you have any flashback or memories of the past, any additional insights, and/or ah-ha thoughts? If so, write them down. Make note of them.

21 – 40 EFT Tapping Statements

The world stands aside to let anyone pass who knows where they are going.

David Jordan

21. It is not polite to be aggressive.

22. I feel threatened by rising stars.

23. I lack the courage to "go for it."

24. I'm too insecure to be powerful.

25. I'm not graceful under pressure.

26. I'm not able to think on my feet.

27. Success is not attainable for me.

28. I don't have faith in my abilities.

29. I have difficulty asserting myself.

30. I don't rebound from my failures.

31. I doubt my instincts and intuition.

32. I am not able to visualize success.

33. Those around me want me to fail.

34. I don't know how to be powerful.

35. I procrastinate and make excuses.

36. I resent others that are successful.

37. I cannot transcend my limitations.

38. I am not committed to excellence.

39. I don't have a strategy for my life.

40. I allow others to walk all over me.

Journaling Pages for Statements 21 – 40

When the grass looks greener on the other side of the
fence, it may be that they take better care of it there.

Cecil Selig

1. From the tapping statements between 1 – 20, list the top seven statements that you thought or felt applied to you:

1.

2.

3.

4.

5.

6.

7.

2. From this list of seven statements, select one and describe how it plays out in your life. Give an example or two. It is important to recognize and identify the pattern. Is there a trigger? How does it begin? How has it benefited you? How has it harmed you? For instance, do you stop at failure? Is this because you have nowhere to go? Is it easier to fail than to stand up again and try?

3. Tap out the top 7 statements.

4. As you were tapping out the statements, did you have any flashback or memories of the past, any additional insights, and/or ah-ha thoughts? If so, write them down. Make note of them.

41 – 60 EFT Tapping Statements

There is no traffic jam on the extra mile.

Business axiom

41. I don't remain true to myself.

42. Success is empty and hollow.

43. I stay down when I fall down.

44. I don't look for opportunities.

45. I don't always keep my word.

46. Joy only comes after success.

47. I expect success immediately.

48. I don't leverage my time well.

49. I am intimidated by obstacles.

50. I don't shape my own destiny.

51. I am not driven to do my best.

52. I'm stuck in analysis paralysis.

53. My identity is that of a failure.

54. I don't use my time efficiently.

55. I lose my focus under pressure.

56. I cannot be trusted with power.

57. I make excuses for my failures.

58. I am not the director of my life.

59. My fears overpower my power.

60. I lack the get-it-done mentality.

Journaling Pages for Statements 41 – 60

Without goals and plans to reach them, you are
like a ship that has set sail with no destination.

Fitzhugh Dodson

1. From the tapping statements between 1 – 20, list the top seven statements that you thought or felt applied to you:

1.

2.

3.

4.

5.

6.

7.

2. From this list of seven statements, select one and describe how it plays out in your life. Give an example or two. It is important to recognize and identify the pattern. Is there a trigger? How does it begin? How has it benefited you? How has it harmed you? For instance, in this day and age of technology, do you expect your successes to happen just as quickly? Do you want your success to happen immediately because you would fail at the "What do I do now to make this work?"

3. Tap out the top 7 statements.

4. As you were tapping out the statements, did you have any flashback or memories of the past, any additional insights, and/or ah-ha thoughts? If so, write them down. Make note of them.

61 – 80 EFT Tapping Statements

The road to success has many tempting parking places.

Steve Potter

61. I lack the integrity to be powerful.

62. I avoid any and all confrontations.

63. Only rich people can be powerful.

64. I focus more on what I don't have.

65. I don't pay attention to the details.

66. I look outside myself for approval.

67. I can't seem to rise above average.

68. I lose focus with a loss and failure.

69. I lack the power to be empowered.

70. It is not safe for me to be powerful.

71. I am too anxious to be empowered.

72. I lack the ability to get things done.

73. Powerful people are control freaks.

74. I don't celebrate my little successes.

75. I get rattled when demands are high.

76. I don't know how to manage money.

77. I sabotage my power and/or success.

78. I quit if I don't succeed immediately.

79. It is not safe to think outside the box.

80. I take setbacks and failure personally.

Journaling Pages for Statements 61 – 80

*People are like stained-glass windows. They sparkle and shine
when the sun is out, but when the darkness sets in their true
beauty is revealed only if there is light from within.*

Elisabeth Kübler-Ross

1. From the tapping statements between 1 – 20, list the top seven statements that you thought or felt applied to you:

1.

2.

3.

4.

5.

6.

7.

2. From this list of seven statements, select one and describe how it plays out in your life. Give an example or two. It is important to recognize and identify the pattern. Is there a trigger? How does it begin? How has it benefited you? How has it harmed you? For instance, does something always sabotages your success and personal power? Have you noticed the one common denominator? That would be you!

3. Tap out the top 7 statements.

4. As you were tapping out the statements, did you have any flashback or memories of the past, any additional insights, and/or ah-ha thoughts? If so, write them down. Make note of them.

81 – 100 EFT Tapping Statements

If you want to improve your self-worth, stop giving other people the calculator.

Tim Fargo

81. I don't try when I know I can't succeed.

82. I lose the small details when I think big.

83. I don't honor my instincts and intuition.

84. I give up when obstacles block my way.

85. I lack the ability to anticipate problems.

86. I don't demand excellence from myself.

87. I don't know how to see the big picture.

88. I avoid anyone that I have an issue with.

89. Others will resent me if I am successful.

90. I am defensive when I receive feedback.

91. Others would be envious of my success.

92. I don't pay attention to the small details.

93. I depend on others to tell me what to do.

94. I am only successful if others think I am.

95. I don't know how to step into my power.

96. My actions and words are not congruent.

97. I am not motivated to do and be my best.

98. I can't figure out what I am doing wrong.

99. I would rather be spiritual than powerful.

100. Power is intimidating and overwhelming.

Journaling Pages for Statements 81 – 100

*You have to set goals that are almost out of reach. If you set
a goal that is attainable without much work or thought, you
are stuck with something below your true talent and potential.*

Steve Garvey

1. From the tapping statements between 1 – 20, list the top seven statements that you thought or felt applied to you:

1.

2.

3.

4.

5.

6.

7.

2. From this list of seven statements, select one and describe how it plays out in your life. Give an example or two. It is important to recognize and identify the pattern. Is there a trigger? How does it begin? How has it benefited you? How has it harmed you? For instance, do you believe you have to choose between being powerful or being spiritual? If so, which do you chose? Being powerful without a conscious or being spiritual and giving up your power?

3. Tap out the top 7 statements.

4. As you were tapping out the statements, did you have any flashback or memories of the past, any additional insights, and/or ah-ha thoughts? If so, write them down. Make note of them.

101 – 120 EFT Tapping Statements

Anytime you poke your head above the crowd,
someone might take a poke at it. Look anyway.

United Technologies

101. I am not committed to doing my best.

102. I'm not calm when there is a problem.

103. It's not okay to out-distance my peers.

104. I lack the persistence to be successful.

105. I don't have the right to be successful.

106. Power and/or success will corrupt me.

107. I lack the courage to live my life fully.

108. I am controlled by my negative habits.

109. I don't give it the absolute best I have.

110. I replay losses over and over and over.

111. I don't do the things I don't like doing.

112. I don't know how to find the solutions.

113. I don't have unshakable determination.

114. Others keep me from being successful.

115. I stop as soon as I endure any hardship.

116. Roadblocks are dead ends, not detours.

117. I would be hounded if I was successful.

118. I am powerless to create the life I want.

119. I lose my determination under pressure.

120. Excellence is a not a way of life for me.

Journaling Pages for Statements 101 – 120

The game of life doesn't build character. It reveals it.

Heywood Broun

1. From the tapping statements between 1 – 20, list the top seven statements that you thought or felt applied to you:

1.

2.

3.

4.

5.

6.

7.

2. From this list of seven statements, select one and describe how it plays out in your life. Give an example or two. It is important to recognize and identify the pattern. Is there a trigger? How does it begin? How has it benefited you? How has it harmed you? For instance, is a roadblock really a dead end or can it be a detour? If you think you are defeated, it becomes a dead end. If you think there can be another way, it's a detour, and you will find another way.

3. Tap out the top 7 statements.

4. As you were tapping out the statements, did you have any flashback or memories of the past, any additional insights, and/or ah-ha thoughts? If so, write them down. Make note of them.

121 – 140 EFT Tapping Statements

*Every job is a self-portrait of the person who
did it. Autograph your work with excellence.*

Jessica Guidobono

121. Whatever I accomplish will be taken away.

122. Disappointment is the signal to stop trying.

123. I don't put action behind my commitments.

124. I don't understand why I am not successful.

125. It is gloating to acknowledge my successes.

126. I make excuses when things don't get done.

127. I don't believe that I can ever be successful.

128. I'm not willing to sacrifice to be successful.

129. I am not organized enough to be successful.

130. I depend on others to determine my actions.

131. My habit of worrying robs me of my power.

132. I lack the fire-in-the-belly desire to succeed.

133. I'm not able to re-chart my path after defeat.

134. Being successful is stressful and exhausting.

135. I have nothing to say during a confrontation.

136. Those around me don't want me to succeed.

137. I lack the discipline needed to be successful.

138. I lack the mental toughness to be successful.

139. I've lost in my mind before I've even begun.

140. I am discouraged by the negativity of others.

Journaling Pages for Statements 121 – 140

Michael Jordan was cut from his high school basketball team. We will not be remembered for the number of times we failed in the beginning, but for the number of times we succeeded in the end.

Edge Keynote

1. From the tapping statements between 1 – 20, list the top seven statements that you thought or felt applied to you:

1.

2.

3.

4.

5.

6.

7.

2. From this list of seven statements, select one and describe how it plays out in your life. Give an example or two. It is important to recognize and identify the pattern. Is there a trigger? How does it begin? How has it benefited you? How has it harmed you? For instance, do you have a plan to accomplish your goals? Is it easier to wander aimlessly through life without a plan, without a direction, without any commitments, never challenging yourself, your talents, and/or your abilities?

3. Tap out the top 7 statements.

4. As you were tapping out the statements, did you have any flashback or memories of the past, any additional insights, and/or ah-ha thoughts? If so, write them down. Make note of them.

141 – 160 EFT Tapping Statements

It's hard to be a diamond in a rhinestone world.

Dolly Parton

141. I'm not grounded enough to be powerful.

142. I can't do what has not been done before.

143. I don't do well with delayed gratification.

144. I will lose my success if I acknowledge it.

145. Success is the answer to all my problems.

146. I don't go the extra mile success requires.

147. Others will not love me if I was powerful.

148. I don't feel empowered and/or successful.

149. I don't let my competence speak for itself.

150. I don't have what it takes to reach the top.

151. I'm angry that I am not already successful.

152. I don't have what it takes to be successful.

153. I'm paralyzed when faced with challenges.

154. I will never be successful and/or powerful.

155. I am a procrastinator unable to take action.

156. I'm waiting for power to be granted to me.

157. I don't know how to strategize for success.

158. Only the strong and powerful can succeed.

159. I lack the desire and drive to be successful.

160. I lack strategic, verbal, and language skills.

Journaling Pages for Statements 141 – 160

Human tragedies: We all want to be extraordinary and we all just want to fit in. Unfortunately, extraordinary people rarely fit in.

Sebastyne Young

1. From the tapping statements between 1 – 20, list the top seven statements that you thought or felt applied to you:

1.

2.

3.

4.

5.

6.

7.

2. From this list of seven statements, select one and describe how it plays out in your life. Give an example or two. It is important to recognize and identify the pattern. Is there a trigger? How does it begin? How has it benefited you? How has it harmed you? For instance, does your lack of success confirm your inadequacy? Is this about self-worth, success, learning new skills, and/or working toward a goal? Or that you lack the tools and skills to be successful?

3. Tap out the top 7 statements.

4. As you were tapping out the statements, did you have any flashback or memories of the past, any additional insights, and/or ah-ha thoughts? If so, write them down. Make note of them.

161 – 180 EFT Tapping Statements

It is amazing how many cares disappear when one decides not to be something but to be someone.

Coco Chanel

161. I lack the preparation part of being successful.

162. I lack the ability to simplify complex subjects.

163. Powerful people are conceited and obnoxious.

164. I am not equipped to handle power or success.

165. The only way I can be powerful is to be angry.

166. I'm waiting for opportunity to come knocking.

167. I don't know how to get to where I want to go.

168. I accept the status quo rather than challenge it.

169. I lack the confidence to achieve difficult goals.

170. Success only brings additional responsibilities.

171. I am not totally committed to being successful.

172. I lack the determination to keep on keeping on.

173. No matter what I do, I will never be successful.

174. I compromise my values so I can be successful.

175. I lack the ability to bring my dreams to fruition.

176. More would be asked of me if I was successful.

177. No one would ever believe that I was powerful.

178. I allow others to rob me of my energy and time.

179. I'm not willing to work hard to get what I want.

180. My friends will abandon me if I was successful.

Journaling Pages for Statements 161 – 180

The will to win, the desire to succeed, the urge to reach your full potential,
these are the keys that will unlock the door to personal excellence.

Confucius

1. From the tapping statements between 1 – 20, list the top seven statements that you thought or felt applied to you:

1.

2.

3.

4.

5.

6.

7.

2. From this list of seven statements, select one and describe how it plays out in your life. Give an example or two. It is important to recognize and identify the pattern. Is there a trigger? How does it begin? How has it benefited you? How has it harmed you? For instance, do you really not have the energy to pursue your goals or do you not have a compelling future to move toward? Do you not have the energy to fulfill your goals or do you give your energy to everyone else other than yourself? Do you not have the energy to succeed or is it safer to fail?

3. Tap out the top 7 statements.

4. As you were tapping out the statements, did you have any flashback or memories of the past, any additional insights, and/or ah-ha thoughts? If so, write them down. Make note of them.

181 – 200 EFT Tapping Statements

*The final proof of greatness lies in being able
to endure criticism without resentment.*

Elbert Hubbard

181. I don't always follow the best plan of action.

182. It is difficult for me to ignore petty criticism.

183. I don't know how to deal with loss or defeat.

184. I'm not comfortable standing out in a crowd.

185. I lack the willpower needed to be successful.

186. I lack the motivation and passion to succeed.

187. I'm not able to produce, perform, or achieve.

188. It's not safe for others for me to be powerful.

189. To be loved, I give up my power and control.

190. Powerful people are mean, cruel, and hurtful.

191. I don't follow through on my tasks and goals.

192. I get impatient waiting for success to happen.

193. I lack the fearlessness it takes to be powerful.

194. I'm not willing to step up to the plate and bat.

195. I lack the technical expertise to be successful.

196. Powerful people are bullies and manipulative.

197. Powerful people are competitive and ruthless.

198. I don't know how to prioritize my "to do" list.

199. I lack the inner resources to survive a setback.

200. I would be laughed at if I tried to be powerful.

Journaling Pages for Statements 181 – 200

The first and greatest obstacle to success for most people is their belief in themselves. Their lack of trust in themselves is a self-imposed limitation.

John Maxwell

1. From the tapping statements between 1 – 20, list the top seven statements that you thought or felt applied to you:

1.

2.

3.

4.

5.

6.

7.

2. From this list of seven statements, select one and describe how it plays out in your life. Give an example or two. It is important to recognize and identify the pattern. Is there a trigger? How does it begin? How has it benefited you? How has it harmed you? For instance, is "try" your middle name? "Try" is an excuse for failure. Is it easier to "try" than to succeed? Is it easier to fail than to succeed?

3. Tap out the top 7 statements.

4. As you were tapping out the statements, did you have any flashback or memories of the past, any additional insights, and/or ah-ha thoughts? If so, write them down. Make note of them.

201 – 220 EFT Tapping Statements

I start where the last man left off.

Thomas Edison

201. I'm not flexible enough to handle the unexpected.

202. I have no clue how to identify what isn't working.

203. It takes too much effort to do my best all the time.

204. I don't know how to resolve unsolvable problems.

205. It is not okay to be proud of my accomplishments.

206. I don't trust that everything will work in my favor.

207. I want instant gratification and immediate payoffs.

208. I don't know how to maneuver around roadblocks.

209. Problems are not opportunities to improve my life.

210. I focus more on my weaknesses than my strengths.

211. I would be called aggressive if I acted empowered.

212. Other people's success is a sign of my own failure.

213. I lack the go-get 'em attitude necessary to succeed.

214. I am not willing to tell my friends of my successes.

215. I don't have unshakable confidence in my abilities.

216. I don't have the capacity to deal with uncertainties.

217. I lack the determination necessary to be successful.

218. It's not okay/safe to be powerful and/or successful.

219. I don't remain cool or level-headed under pressure.

220. My identity is that of "struggle" and not of success.

Journaling Pages for Statements 201 – 220

You miss 100% of the shots you never take.

Wayne Gretzky

1. From the tapping statements between 1 – 20, list the top seven statements that you thought or felt applied to you:

1.

2.

3.

4.

5.

6.

7.

2. From this list of seven statements, select one and describe how it plays out in your life. Give an example or two. It is important to recognize and identify the pattern. Is there a trigger? How does it begin? How has it benefited you? How has it harmed you? For instance, why would you not be willing to share your successes with your friends? Do you think they would be envious and try to sabotage your success? Do you think they would think you were bragging or better than them? Did you select these people to be your friends for a specific reason?

3. Tap out the top 7 statements.

4. As you were tapping out the statements, did you have any flashback or memories of the past, any additional insights, and/or ah-ha thoughts? If so, write them down. Make note of them.

221 – 240 EFT Tapping Statements

Life is not about finding ourselves. Life is about creating ourselves.
George Bernard Shaw

221. I'm hesitant to take the action I know is needed.

222. It is not okay/safe for me to stand up for myself.

223. I don't know how to learn from my experiences.

224. I'm angry that others are successful and I'm not.

225. Only power-hungry people want to be powerful.

226. I am not successful if I allow anyone to help me.

227. My success will disappear as soon as it happens.

228. I don't give 100% to the fulfillment of my goals.

229. I don't know who I would be if I was successful.

230. I don't allow love to be the force that directs me.

231. I have difficulty moving out of my comfort zone.

232. Success is synonymous with gloating and vanity.

233. My life centers around "shoulds" and "have tos."

234. I lack the ability to handle obstacles successfully.

235. I don't want the responsibility of being powerful.

236. Other people will challenge me if I was powerful.

237. It's not possible to be the director of my own life.

238. I'm stopped in my tracks if someone disapproves.

239. I give up when the obstacles seem overwhelming.

240. I don't follow a task through until it is completed.

Journaling Pages for Statements 221 – 240

My son, observe the postage stamp! Its usefulness depends
upon its ability to stick to one thing until it gets there.

Henry Wheeler Shaw

1. From the tapping statements between 1 – 20, list the top seven statements that you thought or felt applied to you:

1.

2.

3.

4.

5.

6.

7.

2. From this list of seven statements, select one and describe how it plays out in your life. Give an example or two. It is important to recognize and identify the pattern. Is there a trigger? How does it begin? How has it benefited you? How has it harmed you? For instance, would too much be expected of you if you were powerful? Would this be an issue of being powerful, confident, fearful, and/or angry?

3. Tap out the top 7 statements.

4. As you were tapping out the statements, did you have any flashback or memories of the past, any additional insights, and/or ah-ha thoughts? If so, write them down. Make note of them.

241 – 260 EFT Tapping Statements

The question isn't who is going to let me; it's who is going to stop me?

Ayn Rand

241. I cannot successfully handle the challenges of success.

242. It is not okay/safe for me to stand out or to be noticed.

243. I lack the confidence to be successful and/or powerful.

244. I don't know how to overcome difficulties or setbacks.

245. I am not able to spot potential problems ahead of time.

246. I must leave everyone behind in order to be successful.

247. I lack the self-esteem to be powerful and/or successful.

248. I feel insecure and uncomfortable around other people.

249. I become very uncomfortable when others criticize me.

250. Others would make fun of me if I tried being powerful.

251. I try to please others rather than voice my own opinion.

252. I'm not able to shrug off criticism and personal attacks.

253. I am not capable of achieving the goals I set for myself.

254. I'm not smart enough to be successful and/or powerful.

255. I don't feel confident in my ability to achieve my goals.

256. My parent wanted me to be what they wanted me to be.

257. My fear robs me of my power, passion, and confidence.

258. I don't create the circumstances I need to be successful.

259. I would not know how to feel about myself if I succeed.

260. I am too irresponsible to be successful and/or powerful.

Journaling Pages for Statements 241 – 260

Excellence is never an accident. It is the result of high intention, sincere effort, intelligent direction, and skillful execution. And the vision to see obstacles as opportunities. It represents the wise choice of many alternatives. Choice, not chance, determines your destiny.

Aristotle

1. From the tapping statements between 1 – 20, list the top seven statements that you thought or felt applied to you:

1.

2.

3.

4.

5.

6.

7.

2. From this list of seven statements, select one and describe how it plays out in your life. Give an example or two. It is important to recognize and identify the pattern. Is there a trigger? How does it begin? How has it benefited you? How has it harmed you? For instance, what do you do when someone is upset with you? Cry? Get angry? Become defensive? Or do you engage in a conversation to understand why they are upset and to find a solution that works for both of you? How do you react when someone else is upset, angry, or shouting? Can you keep your center while someone else has lost theirs? Or do you get drawn into the conflict, become defensive, and angry as well?

3. Tap out the top 7 statements.

4. As you were tapping out the statements, did you have any flashback or memories of the past, any additional insights, and/or ah-ha thoughts? If so, write them down. Make note of them.

261 – 280 EFT Tapping Statements

There are two ways of meeting difficulties. You can alter the difficulties or you can alter yourself meeting them.

Phyllis Bottome

261. Powerful/successful people are ruthless and driven.

262. I lack the courage to be powerful and/or successful.

263. I doubt my ability to be powerful and/or successful.

264. I don't know what to do to create the results I want.

265. I am not committed to living each day to the fullest.

266. It's not okay/safe to be more successful than others.

267. My insecurities keep me from becoming successful.

268. I have a difficult time bouncing back from setbacks.

269. I am not willing to stretch beyond my comfort zone.

270. I don't move forward with sureness and momentum.

271. I can't handle other people's jealousy of my success.

272. I don't live my life the way I would choose to live it.

273. Success is synonymous with hard work and burnout.

274. I open myself up to be attacked when I am powerful.

275. I lack persistence, determination, and follow-through.

276. I would already be successful if I was supposed to be.

277. Success is only about power, money, glory, and fame.

278. I've done everything right and I'm still not successful.

279. I follow the crowd rather than make up my own mind.

280. I don't feel in control when my limits are being tested.

Journaling Pages for Statements 261 – 280

It is not enough to have a dream unless you are willing to pursue it. It is not enough to know what is right unless you are strong enough to do it. It is not enough to learn the truth unless you also learn to live it. It is not enough to reach for love unless you care enough to give it. Men who are resolved to find a way for themselves will always find opportunities enough and if they do not find them, they will make them.

Samuel Smiles

1. From the tapping statements between 1 – 20, list the top seven statements that you thought or felt applied to you:

1.

2.

3.

4.

5.

6.

7.

2. From this list of seven statements, select one and describe how it plays out in your life. Give an example or two. It is important to recognize and identify the pattern. Is there a trigger? How does it begin? How has it benefited you? How has it harmed you? For instance, do you feel there is nothing good about mistakes? Do you have to be perfect and do everything perfectly? Are you so embarrassed when you make a mistake that you are not able to self-correct? Does mistake = failure?

3. Tap out the top 7 statements.

4. As you were tapping out the statements, did you have any flashback or memories of the past, any additional insights, and/or ah-ha thoughts? If so, write them down. Make note of them.

281 – 300 EFT Tapping Statements

The cave you fear to enter holds the treasure you seek.

Joseph Campbell

281. I don't have the courage to face the challenges of my life.

282. I am not consistent and persistent enough to be powerful.

283. I don't know how to make happen what I want to happen.

284. My standards for myself are unreasonable and unrealistic.

285. My self-talk is not encouraging, supportive, or respectful.

286. I am afraid I won't be able to cope with power or success.

287. Powerful/Successful people are mean, rude, and uncaring.

288. I am not able to step up to the plate when the count is 3-2.

289. At crossroads, I choose compromise rather than character.

290. I'm not able to conceptualize how to do what I need to do.

291. I'm not an initiator with the ability to make things happen.

292. I don't take the initiative to be powerful and/or successful.

293. I've lost the fire and passion to do my life with excellence.

294. My life is too busy, scattered, and chaotic to be successful.

295. I'm not assertive enough to be powerful and/or successful.

296. Being powerful and/or successful would make me a target.

297. I lack the tools and skills to be powerful and/or successful.

298. It is not okay/safe for me to be successful and/or powerful.

299. I am only safe when I am less powerful than everyone else.

300. I am not selective as to what I do with my time and energy.

Journaling Pages for Statements 281 – 300

Unsuccessful people make decisions based on their current situation;
successful people make decisions based on where they want to be.

Anonymous

1. From the tapping statements between 1 – 20, list the top seven statements that you thought or felt applied to you:

1.

2.

3.

4.

5.

6.

7.

2. From this list of seven statements, select one and describe how it plays out in your life. Give an example or two. It is important to recognize and identify the pattern. Is there a trigger? How does it begin? How has it benefited you? How has it harmed you? For instance, are your standards realistic? If not, then do you even try? Is this your excuse for not trying? Do you feel empowered to live up to your standards? Or are you too insecure to pursue a higher standard?

3. Tap out the top 7 statements.

4. As you were tapping out the statements, did you have any flashback or memories of the past, any additional insights, and/or ah-ha thoughts? If so, write them down. Make note of them.

301 – 320 EFT Tapping Statements

Success is not final, failure is not fatal. What counts is the courage to continue.
Winston Churchill

301. I lack the patience and tenacity needed to be successful.

302. Power is synonymous with exerting control over others.

303. Power people are controlling, selfish, and self-centered.

304. I will not be able to consistently perform at a high level.

305. I don't know how to evaluate and analyze opportunities.

306. Everything will be perfect after I have achieved success.

307. I am not able to eliminate distractions to maintain focus.

308. I lack the self-worth to be empowered and/or successful.

309. Other people are more successful at what I do than I am.

310. I play it safe rather than take calculated, intelligent risks.

311. I don't have the strength to persist in the face of failures.

312. I don't change my approach if something is not working.

313. Others are superior to me because of their achievements.

314. I don't know how to chuck down my goals to baby steps.

315. It is arrogant to take pride in my achievements and work.

316. I'm too self-destructive to be successful and/or powerful.

317. I don't have the fire and passion needed to be successful.

318. My friends will treat me differently once I am successful.

319. I don't have the courage to be the master of my own fate.

320. I take on more than anyone could reasonably accomplish.

Journaling Pages for Statements 301 – 320

If you truly expect to realize your dreams, abandon the need for blanket approval.
If conforming to everyone's expectations is the number one goal,
you have sacrificed your uniqueness, and therefore your excellence.

Hope Solo

1. From the tapping statements between 1 – 20, list the top seven statements that you thought or felt applied to you:

1.

2.

3.

4.

5.

6.

7.

2. From this list of seven statements, select one and describe how it plays out in your life. Give an example or two. It is important to recognize and identify the pattern. Is there a trigger? How does it begin? How has it benefited you? How has it harmed you? For instance, you can't work toward your goals because everything is not perfect. Our lives will never be perfect. So, is the issue about fulfilling your dreams or perfection?

3. Tap out the top 7 statements.

4. As you were tapping out the statements, did you have any flashback or memories of the past, any additional insights, and/or ah-ha thoughts? If so, write them down. Make note of them.

321 – 340 EFT Tapping Statements

Destiny is not a matter of chance, but a matter of choice.
It is not a thing to wait for, it is a thing to be achieved.

William Jennings Bryan

321. It is beyond my capabilities to be successful and/or powerful.

322. Only those with a title, position, and wealth can be powerful.

323. People in my life encourage me to stay small and play it safe.

324. I don't know how to turn my ideas and/or dreams into reality.

325. Successful and/or powerful people are overbearing and cruel.

326. I am intimidated by the responsibilities of success and power.

327. My friends would not be supportive of me if I was successful.

328. Successful and/or powerful people are unloving and uncaring.

329. I am not able to walk away from distractions and temptations.

330. My parents made demands that no child could possibly fulfill.

331. I am not flexible enough to adjust to any circumstances I face.

332. I will do something stupid and lose it all once I am successful.

333. Everyone will want something from me when I am successful.

334. I don't acknowledge my successes, victories, or achievements.

335. Success and power are synonymous with arrogance and greed.

336. I don't have any way to gauge progress and recognize success.

337. I don't have the confidence to overcome difficulties in my life.

338. Others will be/are threatened by my achievements and success.

339. Being powerful and/or successful would be too overwhelming.

340. I am not willing to do anything without a guarantee of success.

Journaling Pages for Statements 321 – 340

There are no secrets to success. It is the result of preparation,
hard work, and learning from failure.

Colin Powell

1. From the tapping statements between 1 – 20, list the top seven statements that you thought or felt applied to you:

1.

2.

3.

4.

5.

6.

7.

2. From this list of seven statements, select one and describe how it plays out in your life. Give an example or two. It is important to recognize and identify the pattern. Is there a trigger? How does it begin? How has it benefited you? How has it harmed you? For instance, are you resentful of those with the power? Are powerful people uncaring, manipulative, and greedy? If so, do you choose not to be powerful yourself?

3. Tap out the top 7 statements.

4. As you were tapping out the statements, did you have any flashback or memories of the past, any additional insights, and/or ah-ha thoughts? If so, write them down. Make note of them.

341 – 360 EFT Tapping Statements

You can't make footprints in the sand of time if you're sitting on your butt and who wants to make butt prints in the sand of time?

Bob Moawad

341. I don't look for way to develop alternative and better paths.

342. I lack the self-assuredness to be successful and/or powerful.

343. I don't know how to transform my experience into wisdom.

344. I lack the financial wealth to be successful and/or powerful.

345. I am too critical of myself to be successful and/or powerful.

346. I don't have the financial resources needed to be successful.

347. I make too many mistakes to be successful and/or powerful.

348. I have not kept up with technology enough to be successful.

349. I only feel successful when others acknowledge my success.

350. I lack the motivation to continue when the going gets tough.

351. I am not persistent enough to be successful and/or powerful.

352. I don't know what action is necessary to get my life moving.

353. I am not able to maintain optimism in stressful, trying times.

354. I don't have the tools to handle my life after I am successful.

355. My past sins/wrongs prevent me from being successful now.

356. I must be perfect before I can be powerful and/or successful.

357. I lack the fearlessness it takes to be powerful and successful.

358. I don't use past failures to pave the way for future successes.

359. I don't look inward as to what I need to improve for success.

360. I would be abandoned and rejected if I tried to be successful.

Journaling Pages for Statements 341 – 360

*I will love the light for it shows me the way, yet I will
endure the darkness because it shows me the stars.*

Og Mandino

1. From the tapping statements between 1 – 20, list the top seven statements that you thought or felt applied to you:

1.

2.

3.

4.

5.

6.

7.

2. From this list of seven statements, select one and describe how it plays out in your life. Give an example or two. It is important to recognize and identify the pattern. Is there a trigger? How does it begin? How has it benefited you? How has it harmed you? For instance, do you believe you will never have the things you want? Is this because you don't work toward their achievement, you are undeserving, and/or they are unrealistic?

3. Tap out the top 7 statements.

4. As you were tapping out the statements, did you have any flashback or memories of the past, any additional insights, and/or ah-ha thoughts? If so, write them down. Make note of them.

361 – 380 EFT Tapping Statements

Don't wait for your ship to come in. Row out to meet it.

Unknown

361. I lack the intelligence needed to be powerful and/or successful.

362. I don't have the skills needed to be powerful and/or successful.

363. I lack the motivation to do the work necessary to be successful.

364. I have too much mind chatter to be powerful and/or successful.

365. I don't have the talents, abilities, or know-how to be successful.

366. I have too many inner demons to be successful and/or powerful.

367. Success and power is synonymous with arrogant and better than.

368. I would be called obnoxious if I was powerful and/or successful.

369. I'm slow to change direction even when the situation warrants it.

370. I lack the ability to rise above my circumstances to be successful.

371. My friends and family will treat me differently if I am successful.

372. I am not committed to doing the work necessary to be successful.

373. I must achieve all my successes by myself with help from no one.

374. Once I succeed I will be under tremendous pressure to be perfect.

375. I don't have the abilities needed to be powerful and/or successful.

376. I would be called controlling and selfish if I tried to be successful.

377. I don't have the qualities needed to be successful and/or powerful.

378. I don't go back to the fundamentals when things start to go wrong.

379. There are too many obstacles for me to overcome to be successful.

380. I don't have the boldness needed to be successful and/or powerful.

Journaling Pages for Statements 361 – 380

We are all faced with a series of great opportunities
brilliantly disguised as unsolvable problems.

John W. Gardner

1. From the tapping statements between 1 – 20, list the top seven statements that you thought or felt applied to you:

1.

2.

3.

4.

5.

6.

7.

2. From this list of seven statements, select one and describe how it plays out in your life. Give an example or two. It is important to recognize and identify the pattern. Is there a trigger? How does it begin? How has it benefited you? How has it harmed you? For instance, when faced with challenges, where is your focus? Are you too paralyzed to even think? Do you lack the confidence to successfully meet the challenge or is it courage that you lack?

3. Tap out the top 7 statements.

4. As you were tapping out the statements, did you have any flashback or memories of the past, any additional insights, and/or ah-ha thoughts? If so, write them down. Make note of them.

381 – 400 EFT Tapping Statements

Action without planning is fatal but planning without action is futile.

Tracie Van Eimeren

381. I cannot be more powerful than my parents/partner/spouse/friends.

382. I don't know what action I need to take to accomplish what I want.

383. I lack a calmness that would allow me to focus on the task at hand.

384. I run in the opposite direction when I am confronted with adversity.

385. I am not able to handle the changes success would create in my life.

386. I'm not able to take abstract ideas and turn them into tangible plans.

387. I drive my life with one foot on the gas pedal, the other on the brake.

388. Success and/or power is synonymous with manipulation and control.

389. Successful and/or powerful people are thoughtless and self-centered.

390. I don't know how to turn my aspirations into action in the real world.

391. I would be called aggressive and obnoxious if I tried to be successful.

392. Everyone's needs will be more important than mine if I was powerful.

393. I am not able to express myself in a way that helps me get what I need.

394. Success and/or power are synonymous with loneliness and being alone.

395. I don't take the risks that are necessary to be successful and/or powerful.

396. Others would make fun of me if I tried being successful and/or powerful.

397. I have difficulty staying the course when something unexpected happens.

398. I care too much about what others think to be powerful and/or successful.

399. I am too unhappy, insecure, and negative to be successful and/or powerful.

400. Being successful and/or powerful would bring more problems than I can handle.

Journaling Pages for Statements 381 – 400

A kite flies best when the wind blows in one direction and the string pulls from another.

Henry Ford

1. From the tapping statements between 1 – 20, list the top seven statements that you thought or felt applied to you:

1.

2.

3.

4.

5.

6.

7.

2. From this list of seven statements, select one and describe how it plays out in your life. Give an example or two. It is important to recognize and identify the pattern. Is there a trigger? How does it begin? How has it benefited you? How has it harmed you? For instance, do you try to please everyone all the time? Do you make decision-making difficult because you don't know how to handle the objections by others? Is this a lack of trust in yourself, self-confidence, or self-worth?

3. Tap out the top 7 statements.

4. As you were tapping out the statements, did you have any flashback or memories of the past, any additional insights, and/or ah-ha thoughts? If so, write them down. Make note of them.

ABOUT THE AUTHOR – TESSA CASON, MA

I have been fortunate to have had a number of successful professional lives. In each of these endeavors, it provided the opportunity to observe someone's behavior, actions, reactions, habits, thoughts, feelings, choices, and decisions. Understanding who we are, how we became who we are, and how to change into who we want to become has been a fascinating area of study and research for me for 50 years.

As a swim coach and instructor of 10 and under kids, I had the opportunity to teach and train small children. As an instructor of PE at San Diego State University and Grossmont College, I had the opportunity to interact with and teach college-age individuals. As an owner of a gift company, I had the opportunity to work with business professionals. Belonging to a breakfast group called The Inside Edge and staffing events for The Learning Annex, I was able to interact with and observe the elite authors, speakers, and politicians. Managing a medical clinic provided the opportunity to interact with and observe the seriously ill, some terminal.

In 1977, as a hobby, I started a company that manufactured greeting cards and stationery. Eight years later, my company was grossing a million dollars in sale/year on 50 cent greeting cards.

When my business was grossing a million dollars in sale, I purchased a newly constructed townhouse in La Jolla. Unbeknownst to me, a natural gas pipe was severed during construction and not properly repaired. The gas leak went undetected for 2 1/2 years, 850 days. By then, my health was permanently damaged.

After the gas leak was discovered, all the doctors told me I would be environmentally ill for the rest of my life and would never be able to participate or function in the real world. Not believing the doctors, I set upon a course to discover alternative health treatments. Several years later, while still working on my health, I was managing an alternative health clinic. While working at the clinic, I was able to make the correlation between a patient's emotions and beliefs with their physical illnesses.

In 1996, after thirty years of book reading, psychology classes, metaphysical classes, lectures, and observation, I applied my knowledge and skills into a life coaching practice. I thoroughly enjoyed being a Transformational Life Coach, helping others find clarity in their lives.

Only one problem. It was this: The clients were not completing their assigned tasks that together we had decided they would do as their homework. Even though the clients knew what to do and wanted to do the tasks, somehow the tasks were not getting completed.

Knowing that all of our actions and reactions, thoughts and feelings, choices and decisions are based on our beliefs, I went searching for a tool that would change dysfunctional beliefs. I visited a friend that managed a bookstore and told her my dilemma and that I was in need of a tool, process, or technique that would change dysfunctional beliefs. She reached for a book that was on the counter, informing me that this new addition for them was flying off the shelves and their customers were raving about. It was a book on EFT (Emotional Freedom Technique) Tapping.

I read the book and ordered the videos. Even though I was intrigued, I had no clue how tapping my head could change dysfunctional beliefs or our lives. I had some adventuresome clients (and forgiving if need be) that I taught how to tap.

When every single client returned for their next appointment and shared how different their lives had been that week because of tapping, I took notice! My curiosity was peaked. I then put a lot of time and energy into figuring out how this powerful transformational tool, EFT Tapping, worked and how to best utilize EFT Tapping.

I soon realized working with my clients that the most important aspect of EFT Tapping was the statement that is said as we tap. I also realized that some of the statements I wrote up for one client could be used for another. My clients wanted homework, wanted tapping statements to do on their own. I started a library of EFT Tapping statements that I wrote out for my client as their homework.

In 2005 I was diagnosed with thyroid cancer. While researching thyroid cancer, I discovered that 20 years after exposure to natural gas, thyroid issues would result. It was 20 years nearly to the month that I started having thyroid issues.

From the time I was diagnosed and had surgery, those 6 weeks I only focused on the emotional issues associated with the thyroid and tapped. I did not pursue any other treatments, supplements, or therapies in the 6 weeks leading up to the surgery other than EFT Tapping.

In the recovery room after surgery, the surprised doctor told me that even though two different labs came back with the diagnoses of cancer, it was not cancer. I knew the tapping had changed the energy of the cancer and it no longer was cancer.

Our lives don't change until we change our programming...the beliefs on a subconscious level. EFT Tapping is one of the most powerful techniques I found that could do just that: change our beliefs on a subconscious level.

After surgery, knowing the power of EFT Tapping, knowing the significance of the tapping statement, and knowing that beliefs precede all of our thoughts and feelings, choices and decisions, actions, reactions, and experiences, I created 43 Books for Practitioners and 43 Workbooks for Everyone that were filled with mis-belief, dysfunctional EFT tapping statements.

I am revamping the Workbooks. In the revamped Workbooks, I am combining tapping statements for 5 different topics in each theme-book to heal the issue as completely as possible.

I also have a series of "EFT Tapping Statement" Kindle eBooks on Amazon.

My two greatest joys are helping those that want to grow, evolve, and transform their lives and train others to be transformational coaches!

Books and Kindles eBooks by Tessa Cason

80 EFT TAPPING STATEMENTS FOR:
Abandonment
Abundance, Wealth, Money
Addictions
Adult Children of Alcoholics
Anger and Frustration
Anxiety and Worry
Change
"Less Than" and Anxiety
Manifesting a Romantic Relationship
Relationship with Self
Self Esteem
Social Anxiety
Weight and Emotional Eating

100 EFT Tapping Statements for Accepting Our Uniqueness and Being Different
100 EFT Tapping Statements for Fear of Computers
100 EFT Tapping Statements for I'm Not Extraordinary!
200 EFT Tapping Statements for Healing a Broken Heart
200 EFT Tapping Statements for Knowing God
200 EFT Tapping Statements for Procrastination
200 EFT Tapping Statements for PTSD
200 EFT Tapping Statements for Wealth
240 EFT Tapping Statements for Fear
300 EFT Tapping Statements for Healing the Self
300 EFT Tapping Statements for Dealing with Obnoxious People
300 EFT Tapping Statements for Self-defeating Behavior, Self-pity, Victim
340 EFT Tapping Statements for Healing From the Loss of a Loved One
400 EFT Tapping Statements for Being a Champion
400 EFT Tapping Statements for Dealing with Emotions

400 EFT Tapping Statements for Dreams to Reality
400 EFT Tapping Statements for My Thyroid Story
500 EFT Tapping Statements for Moving Out of Survival

700 EFT Tapping Statements for Weight, Emotional Eating, and Food Cravings
All Things EFT Tapping Manual
Emotional Significance of Human Body Parts
Muscle Testing – Obstacles and Helpful Hints
EFT TAPPING STATEMENTS FOR:
A Broken Heart, Abandonment, Anger, Depression, Grief, Emotional Healing
Anxiety, Fear, Anger, Self Pity, Change
Champion, Success, Personal Power, Self Confidence, Leader/Role Model
PTSD, Disempowered, Survival, Fear, Anger
Weight & Food Cravings, Anger, Grief, Not Good Enough, Failure

OTHER BOOKS
Why we Crave What We Crave: The Archetypes of Food Cravings
How to Heal Our Food Cravings

EFT WORKBOOK AND JOURNAL FOR EVERYONE:
Abandonment
Abundance, Money, Prosperity
Addictions
Adult Children of Alcoholics
Anger, Apathy, Guilt
Anxiety/Worry
Being A Man
Being, Doing, Belonging
Champion
Change
Conflict
Courage
Dark Forces
Decision Making
Depression
Difficult/Toxic Parents
Difficult/Toxic People
Emotional Healing
Fear
Forgiveness
God
Grief
Happiness/Joy

Intuition
Leadership
Live Your Dreams
Life Purpose/Mission
People Pleaser
Perfectionism
Personal Power
Relationship w/Others
Relationship w/Self & Commitment to Self
Self Confidence
Self Worth/Esteem
Sex
Shame
Stress
Success
Survival
Transitions
Trust/Discernment
Victim, Self-pity, Self-Defeating Behavior, Shadow Self
Weight and Emotional Eating

Mis-belief EFT Statements for Practitioners:

Abandonment
Abundance, Money, Prosperity
Addictions
Adult Children of Alcoholics
Anger, Apathy, Guilt
Anxiety/Worry
Being A Man
Being, Doing, Belonging
Champion
Change
Conflict
Courage
Dark Forces
Decision Making
Depression
Difficult/Toxic Parents
Difficult/Toxic People
Emotional Healing
Fear

Forgiveness
God
Grief
Happiness/Joy
Intuition
Leadership
Live Your Dreams
Life Purpose/Mission
People Pleaser
Perfectionism
Personal Power
Relationship w/Others
Relationship w/Self & Commitment w/Self
Self Confidence
Self Worth/Esteem
Sex
Shame
Stress
Success
Survival
Transitions
Trust/Discernment
Victim, Self-pity, Self-Defeating Behavior, Shadow Self
Weight and Emotional Eating

With Gratitude and Appreciation

There are several people I would like to thank:

* I am thankful for Roger Callahan's, Gary Craig's, and Pat Carrington's work developing TFT and EFT. Without their willingness to break the mold, we might still be lying on the couch telling our stories rather than healing our hearts and mis-beliefs.

* I am very thankful for my clients in 2000 that were willing to try something new, something untested, something that was outside the norm. I learned so much watching their growth and evolution.

* I am thankful for Nick Ortner and The Tapping Solution. Nick is willing to defend EFT Tapping and brave the way for the rest of us.

* I am thankful for the research that Dawson Church has put into legitimizing EFT Tapping.

* I am thankful for all the practitioners and people that believe and continue to tap even though it is not quite widely accepted yet.

The End

Made in the USA
Coppell, TX
22 November 2020